Name: Hafsah

Essential Exam Practice

With Answers

Key Stage 3
Tiers 3–5 & 4–6

Ruso Bradley, June Hall and Mark Haslam

Introduction

Mathematics is a subject where practice is the key to success. There is no better way of boosting your level than practising the type of questions that will come up in your SATs. It is no secret that many questions come up year after year, which is why the *Essential Exam Practice* range concentrates on these extremely important questions. It is also true that you can't predict exactly what will be in your SATs, but if you try all the questions in this book, you are unlikely to get any nasty surprises!

About this book

This book is aimed at candidates taking the 3–5 or 4–6 Tier in the Key Stage 3 National Tests (SATs) for Mathematics.

The questions are split into four main sections:
- Number (N)
- Algebra (A)
- Shape, Space & Measures (S)
- Handling Data (H)

Within these sections, the questions are grouped by topic, so you can quickly find what you're looking for. Answers to all questions can be found at the back of the book, so you can check that you're on the right track. There is also a Mental Mathematics Test to try – carefully follow the instructions on page 87.

Instructions

 This means show your working and write down your answer.

 You **may** use a calculator to answer any question with this symbol.

 You **must not** use a calculator to answer any question with this symbol.

If there is no calculator or non-calculator symbol, try the question without a calculator first, then use a calculator to check your answer.

To answer some of the questions in this book, you will need an angle measurer or protractor, tracing paper, a pair of compasses and a calculator. There is a formulae sheet on page 95 to help you.

Good luck in your tests!

Contents

Number

WRITING NUMBERS AS WORDS

N1   Circle the card that shows two hundred and sixty-four.

462   264

   246   426

(1 mark)

N2   Write these numbers in words.

555   ....

   17   ....

5008   ....

   159   ....

(2 marks)

ORDERING NUMBERS & PLACE VALUE

N3

64

15

27   9   101

99

Put these numbers in order, smallest first.

(1 mark)

N4 Put these numbers in the right place on the number line.

1.3   0.5   1.8   0.9   0.3

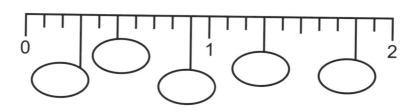

(2 marks)

N5 Put these numbers in order, smallest first:

10.25   20.51   11.25   15.21

.... *(1 mark)*

N6 Which is larger, 19.91 or 19.191?  .... *(1 mark)*

N7 Put these decimals in order, starting with the smallest.

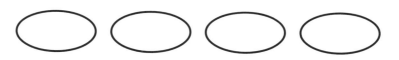

| 1.5 | 11.25 | 1.125 | 12 |

(1 mark)

N8 Ross has three numbered cards.   6   1   8

(a) Rearrange the cards to make the largest possible number.

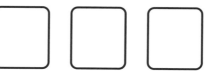

(1 mark)

(b) What is the smallest number Ross can make using all three cards?

(1 mark)

Number

N9 These cards can be reordered to give Rachel's bank balance.

(a) What is the maximum amount that Rachel could have in her bank account?

(1 mark)

(b) What is the least amount that Rachel could have in her bank account?

£ ⬜ ⬜ . ⬜ ⬜

(1 mark)

ADDING & SUBTRACTING

 N10 Draw lines to match the answers to the sums.
For example, 15 + 11 = 26.

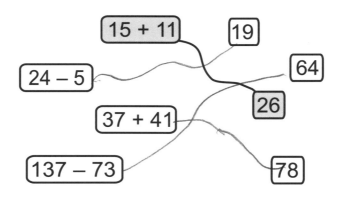

15 + 11   19
24 − 5   64
37 + 41   26
137 − 73   78

(1 mark)

 N11 An express delivery van contains 27 parcels.

(a) How many parcels are there in the van if 49 more parcels are loaded?

.............26............ parcels *(1 mark)*

6

(b) The van is able to deliver 49 parcels in the morning. How many parcels are left?

.......27........ parcels *(1 mark)*

N12 Dave cuts 8.5 cm of rope from a piece of length 14.4 cm. How much rope is left?

..........5·9............ cm *(1 mark)*

N13 Here is the front view of a house with an extension:

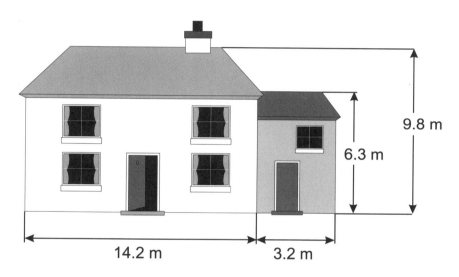

9.8 m

6.3 m

14.2 m   3.2 m

(a) How wide is the house and extension combined?

...33.5............... m *(1 mark)*

(b) How much taller than the extension is the rest of the house?

 .... m *(1 mark)*

Number

N14 Complete these multiplication squares:

×	1	3	5
2			
4			20
8			

×	3	7	9
4			
7			
10			

(2 marks)

N15 There are 12 jars of marmalade in a box.

    (a) How many jars in 4 boxes?

.... jars *(1 mark)*

    (b) How many jars in 12 boxes?

.... jars *(1 mark)*

N16 In a large greenhouse there are 6 rows of rose bushes.
Altogether there are 84 rose bushes in the greenhouse.

How many rose bushes are there in each row?

......................bushes *(1 mark)*

N17 Harvey needs to order 40 tubs of margarine for his sandwich business.
The tubs come in boxes of 7. Harvey estimates that he will need 280 boxes.

    (a) Without working out the correct answer, explain why Harvey is wrong.

(1 mark)

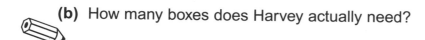

 (b) How many boxes does Harvey actually need?

.... boxes *(1 mark)*

 (c) How many tubs will Harvey have left over?

.... tubs *(1 mark)*

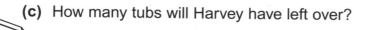

N18 Two cards are related if one is ten times bigger than the other.
Draw loops around all such pairs of cards.

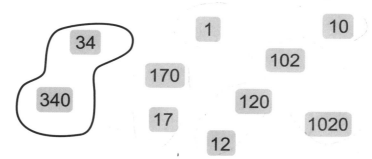

(2 marks)

N19 Fill in the missing numbers:

(a) 16 × 100 = ☐   **(b)** 12 × 1000 = ☐

(c) 65 × ☐ = 650   **(d)** 65 × ☐ = 6500

(2 marks)

N20 Fill in the missing numbers:

(a) 500 ÷ 10 = ☐   **(b)** 5600 ÷ 100 = ☐

(c) 3300 ÷ ☐ = 33   **(d)** 45500 ÷ ☐ = 455   *(2 marks)*

Number

MULTIPLYING & DIVIDING BY 10, 100, 1000

N21 Vincent thinks of a number. He multiplies his number by 100, and then divides it by 100. His answer is 7.

(a) What number did he first think of?

.... *(1 mark)*

Charlotte thinks of a number. She multiplies it by 10, and then by 100. She then divides by 1000. Her answer is 33.

(b) What number did she first think of?

.... *(1 mark)*

LONG MULTIPLICATION & DIVISION

N22 In a high street shop, electronic notebooks cost £343.

(a) Using a suitable method of long multiplication, work out the cost of 16 notebooks.

£ .... *(1 mark)*

The same electronic notebooks are advertised on the internet for £285.

(b) How much would you save if you bought 16 notebooks on the internet instead of the high street?

£ .... *(2 marks)*

N23 Joanne earns £585 a week from the advertising banners on her website. There are 13 banners on her website.

(a) In one week, how much does she earn per banner?

£.................................. *(1 mark)*

(b) How much would she earn if she increased the number of banners on her website to 16? Use your answer to part **(a)**.

£.................................. *(1 mark)*

Last week there were 3514 visitors to Joanne's website.

(c) How many visitors did she get per day?

.... *(1 mark)*

Number

MONEY CALCULATIONS

N24 Envelopes cost 7p each.
Simone buys 20 envelopes.

(a) How much does Simone spend on envelopes?

£ 1.40 .... *(1 mark)* ✓

(b) How much change does she get from £5?

£ 360 .... *(1 mark)* ✓

(c) How many envelopes could she have bought with £5?

6

£ 60 71 .... *(1 mark)* ✓

N25 David works 25 hours each week.
He is paid £6.20 per hour

(a) How much is he paid for a week's work?

£ 1.55 .... *(1 mark)* ✗

David's rent is £50 per week.
After paying his rent and buying some groceries, David has £65 left.

(b) How much does David spend on groceries?

£ 40 .... *(1 mark)* ✓

N26 Abdul has £70 to spend. He needs to buy a bag and a pair of shoes.

Stereo £25.80

Shirt £15.50

Shoes £39.99

Bag £8.95

Belt £14.49

(a) What else can he afford to buy?

............Shirt............ or ....bolt............ ✓ *(2 marks)*

Abdul dislikes the bag and decides not to buy it.

(b) Which different items should he buy to spend as much of his remaining money as possible?

............Shirt............ ✓ and ....bolt........ 2p..... *(1 mark)*

N27 A supermarket sells coffee in three different sizes: 100 g, 200 g and 300 g.

VALUECAFE QUICK ROAST 100 g

£2.50

VALUECAFE QUICK ROAST 200 g

£3.95

VALUECAFE QUICK ROAST 300 g

£6.10

Some supermarkets show the price per 100 g to compare products.

(a) Work out the cost per 100 g for each jar of coffee.

£2.50, £.1.98..................., £.2.03........... ✓ *(2 marks)*

(b) Which jar is the best value? ....200........ g *(1 mark)*

(c) Which jar is the worst value? ....100........ g ✓ *(1 mark)*

Number

N28 What fraction of this shape is shaded?

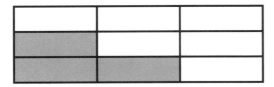

.... (1 mark) ✓

$\frac{1}{3}$

N29 Under the rules of a sailing competition, $\frac{1}{4}$ of a yacht's sail must be shaded.

Shade in $\frac{1}{4}$ of this yacht's sail.

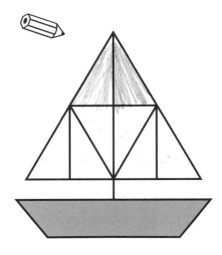

(1 mark)

N30 4 cakes are divided between 6 people.

(a) How much cake does each person get?
Give your answer as a fraction of a cake.

$\frac{2}{3}$

.... *(1 mark)* ✓

There are now 12 people, but still only 4 cakes.

(b) What fraction of a cake does each person now get?

$\frac{1}{3}$

.... *(1 mark)* ✓

N31 Each number in a square box is $\frac{2}{5}$ of a number in a round box. For example, 10 is $\frac{2}{5}$ of 25.

Match the remaining square boxes to the round boxes by drawing connecting lines.

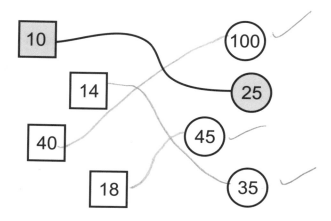

(2 marks)

N32 A farmer has 140 sheep. He marks $\frac{3}{4}$ of them with red dye. The rest of the sheep are marked with green dye.

(a) How many sheep are marked with red dye?

.... 105 .... *(1 mark)*

(b) How many sheep are marked with green dye?

.... 35 .... *(1 mark)*

Number

FRACTIONS

N33 Circle all the cards that show a fraction equivalent to $\frac{2}{3}$.

$\frac{1}{3}$	$\frac{4}{6}$	$\frac{12}{18}$	$\frac{6}{9}$	$\frac{12}{13}$	$\frac{20}{30}$

(1 mark) ✓

N34 Sam has worked out some fraction sums, but one of them is wrong.

(a) Put a cross in the box next to the sum that is wrong.

$$\frac{1}{2} + \frac{1}{4} = \frac{3}{4} \qquad \square$$

$$\frac{1}{5} + \frac{2}{10} = \frac{3}{15} \qquad \boxtimes \checkmark$$

$$\frac{1}{3} + \frac{2}{6} = \frac{2}{3} \qquad \square$$

(1 mark)

(b) Work out the correct answer to the sum that Sam got wrong.

$\frac{2}{5}$

.... *(1 mark)* ✓

N35 There are 24 sheep in a pen. 8 of them are marked with blue dye. The rest of the sheep are marked with orange dye.

(a) Write down the fraction of sheep that are marked with blue dye.
Give your answer in its lowest terms.

$\frac{1}{3}$

.... *(1 mark)* ✓

(b) What fraction of the sheep are marked with orange dye?
Give your answer in its lowest terms.

$\frac{2}{3}$

.... *(1 mark)* ✓

N36 Match these decimals to the amount of each shape that is shaded.

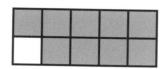

(a) 0.9

(b) 0.5

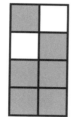 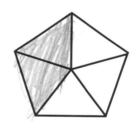

(c) 0.75

(d) 0.2

(2 marks)

N37 Shade these diagrams to show the decimal.

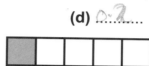

0.25   0.4   0.75

(2 marks)

N38 Find the missing decimals.

(a) 10.86 − 9.43 = 1.43

(b) 3.22 + 1.66 = 4.88

(c) 20 − 9.5 = 10.5

(d) 10.52 + 5.25 = 15.77

(2 marks)

Number

N39 Work out:

 **(a)** 27.69 + 19.95

.... *(1 mark)*

 **(b)** 58.6 + 14.77

.... *(1 mark)*

 **(c)** 33.11 – 4.5

.... *(1 mark)*

(d) 26.3 – 17.21

.... *(1 mark)*

N40 Choose the card that makes each calculation correct.

$$\boxed{10} \qquad \boxed{100}$$

(a) 5.8 × $\boxed{}$ = 580

(b) 5800 ÷ $\boxed{}$ = 58

(c) 0.58 × $\boxed{}$ = 58

(d) 5.8 ÷ $\boxed{}$ = 0.58

(2 marks)

N41 What is 14.18 × 3?

.... *(1 mark)*

N42 What is 93.8 ÷ 7?

.... *(1 mark)*

N43 Use these numbers to fill the gaps:

10   31.26   2.61   30.6   100   7.33

(a) 6.12 × 5 = ...   **(b)** 15.63 × 2 = ...

(c) 21.99 ÷ 3 = ...   **(d)** 5.22 ÷ 2 = ...

(e) 68.9 ÷ .... = 6.89   **(f)** 4.92 × .... = 492

(3 marks)

N44 Find:

(a) 10 × 6.72   .... *(1 mark)*

(b) 20 × 6.72   .... *(1 mark)*

(c) 200 × 6.72   .... *(1 mark)*

Number

N45 An artist thinks that shapes look best when they are 25% shaded in.

(a) Place a tick in the box below each shape that has 25% shaded.

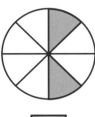 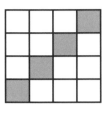 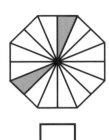

(1 mark)

Another artist think that shapes look better when they are 75% shaded.

(b) Shade 75% of each of these shapes:

 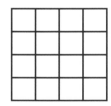 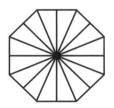

(2 marks)

N46 The fractions, decimals and percentages in each row of this table are equal.

Fill in the blank spaces.

Fraction	Decimal	Percentage
	0.1	10%
$\frac{1}{5}$		20%
		25%
	0.5	
$\frac{3}{4}$		
	0.9	

(4 marks)

N47 Bryan has a gold discount card for a sports shop.
He gets a 10% discount when he uses it.

How much is the discount when he buys:

(a) a pair of football boots marked at £50?

£................................. *(1 mark)*

(b) a skipping rope marked at £7?

£................................. (1 mark)

(c) a *Weightmaster Deluxe* marked at £450?

£................................. *(1 mark)*

Bryan's friend Sue has a platinum discount card for the same sports shop.
She gets a 12% discount when she uses it.

How much is the discount when she buys:

(d) a gum shield priced at £5?

£................................. *(1 mark)*

(e) a golf bag priced at £50?

£................................. *(1 mark)*

Number

N48 The table shows Fiona's scores in six school tests in different subjects.

Complete the percentage column.

Subject	Fiona's score	Total marks available	Percentage
Maths	30	50	60%
English	55	100	
Science	3	10	
Art	120	200	
French	26	40	
Information Technology	38.5	70	

(4 marks)

N49 A music shop is having a sale.

FLUTE £160

GUITAR £90

VIOLIN £220

Every item in the shop is reduced by 20% from the original prices shown.

Find the sale price of

(a) the guitar,

£.............................. *(2 marks)*

22

(b) the flute,

£............................... *(2 marks)*

(c) the violin.

£............................... *(2 marks)*

In an effort to clear old stock, the music shop increases the reduction on the original prices to 34%.

(d) Find the new sale price of the guitar.

£............................... *(2 marks)*

A drum machine was originally priced at £120. Its sale price is £102.

(e) By what percentage was the drum machine reduced?

.... % *(2 marks)*

Number

PERCENTAGES

N50 The fractions, decimals and percentages in each row of this table are equal.

Fill in the blank spaces.

Fraction	Decimal	Percentage
$\frac{1}{20}$		
	0.35	
		37.5%
$\frac{5}{8}$		
	0.64	
		74%

(6 marks)

SPECIAL NUMBERS

N51 (a) Write down the first five square numbers.

.... *(1 mark)*

(b) Write down the first five prime numbers.

.... *(1 mark)*

N52

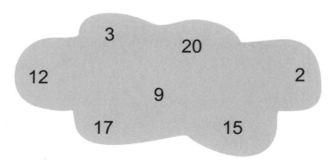

Which of these numbers are

(a) multiples of 4? .... *(1 mark)*

(b) factors of 12? .... *(1 mark)*

(c) prime numbers? .... *(1 mark)*

N53

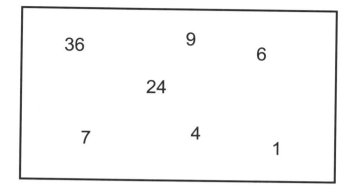

36   9   6

24

7   4

1

(a) Circle all the multiples of 3.

(1 mark)

(b) Draw a square around each square number.

(1 mark)

(c) Which numbers are multiples of 3 and square?

.... *(1 mark)*

N54 Using the $\sqrt{}$ button on your calculator, find the square root of:

(a) 81 .... *(1 mark)*

(b) 225 .... *(1 mark)*

(c) 67.24 .... *(1 mark)*

(d) 151.29 .... *(1 mark)*

Number

N55 Join each of these numbers to its correct position on the number line. The first one has been done for you.

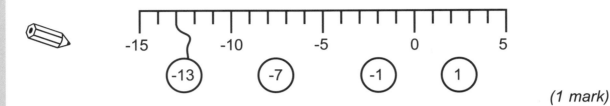

(1 mark)

N56 Choose the < or > sign to order each pair of negative numbers.

(a) -8 ☐ -9

(b) -2 ☐ -1

(c) -30 ☐ -20

(d) -6 ☐ -15

(2 marks)

N57

```
-20   -15   -10   -5   0   5   10   15   20
```

Use the number line to help you match these answers to the questions below:

11   ⁻10   ⁻20   ⁻5   ⁻3   14

(a) $3 - 8$ .... *(1 mark)*

(b) $7 + {}^-10$ .... *(1 mark)*

(c) ${}^-4 + {}^-6$ .... *(1 mark)*

(d) $9 - {}^-5$ .... *(1 mark)*

(e) ${}^-1 - {}^-12$ .... *(1 mark)*

(f) ${}^-15 - 5$ .... *(1 mark)*

N58 **(a)** On the diagram, write down the temperatures indicated on the thermometer.

(b) What is the difference between these two temperatures?

..................°C

(c) The highest temperature indicated is raised by 10°C. Show the new temperature on the diagram.

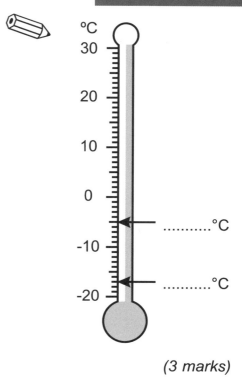

(3 marks)

N59 These ratios may all look different but actually some are the same.

3:9	14:28	5:15
6:10	2:6	12:36	12:20

(a) Draw circles around the ratios that are the same as 1:3.

(2 marks)

(b) Draw squares around the ratios that are the same as 3:5.

(2 marks)

(c) Write in its simplest form any ratio that you have not drawn either a circle or square around.

.... *(1 mark)*

Number

N60 Fill in the missing numbers in these ratio statements.

The ratio 2:3:6 is the same as 4: [   ] : [   ]

The ratio 1: [   ] :7 is the same as 3:12: [   ]

The ratio 2: [   ] :5:11 is the same as 6:9: [   ] : [   ]

(3 marks)

N61 In a supermarket warehouse, the ratio of bags of red potatoes to bags of white potatoes is 2:5.
There are 350 bags of potatoes in the supermarket warehouse.

(a) How many bags of red potatoes are there?

.... bags *(2 marks)*

(b) How many bags of white potatoes are there?

.... bags *(1 mark)*

N62 During a training run, the ratio of the time an athlete spends running on the flat to running uphill to running downhill is 5:2:2.
The training run lasts 54 minutes.

(a) How long does the athlete spend running on the flat?

.... minutes *(2 marks)*

(b) How long does the athlete spend running either uphill or downhill?

.... minutes *(1 mark)*

N63 Complete this table by rounding to the nearest 10. The first line has been completed for you.

Number of pies	Number of pies to the nearest 10
37	40
13	
66	
42	
144	
75	

(3 marks)

N64 Round these numbers to the nearest 100.

(a) 105 ....   (b) 342 ....

(c) 425 ....   (d) 587 ....

(e) 2392 ....   (f) 550 ....

(3 marks)

Number

N65 The number of shoppers that visited a new shopping centre during its first week are given in the table below.

Number of visitors to Lightway Shopping Centre

Day	Number of visitors	Number of visitors to the nearest 1000
Sunday	9392	
Monday	7828	
Tuesday	5539	
Wednesday	3998	
Thursday	7299	
Friday	11 290	
Saturday	14 599	

(a) Complete the table by rounding each number to the nearest 1000.

(3 marks)

(b) To the nearest 1000, how many more people visited the shopping centre on Saturday than Wednesday?

.... *(1 mark)*

N66 Round each of these to the nearest whole number.

(a) 2.7 ....

(b) 5.2 ....

(c) 27.5 ....

(d) 2.76 ....

(e) 23.23 ....

(f) 55.55 ....

(3 marks)

N67 Here are some prices from the *Super Hammer* hardware shop.

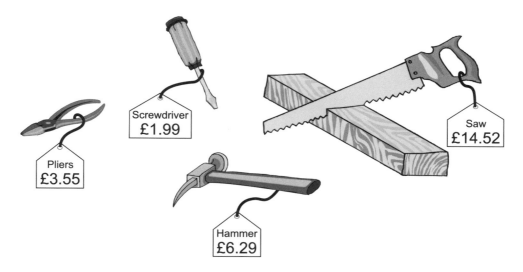

(a) Round each of the prices to the nearest pound.

Hammer = £....................   Saw = £....................

Screwdriver = £....................   Pliers = £....................

(2 marks)

(b) Round each of the prices to the nearest 10p.

Hammer = £....................   Saw = £....................

Screwdriver = £....................   Pliers = £....................

(2 marks)

N68 Round each of these decimals to the nearest tenth.

(a) 1.38 ....   **(b)** 0.43 ....

(c) 0.75 ....   **(d)** 14.74 ....

(e) 1.838 ....   **(f)** 93.99 ....

(3 marks)

Number

ROUNDING & ESTIMATING

N69 Round these numbers to one decimal place.

(a) 1.43 ....

(b) 9.91 ....

(c) 4.88 ....

(d) 7.65 ....

(3 marks)

N70 Professor Goodman is a lazy mathematician. He never works out sums exactly – he always makes an approximation.

For example, to work out $\frac{913 - 104}{78}$ he would round the numbers so that they were easy to work with:

$\frac{900 - 100}{80} = 800 \div 80 = 10$

Following the example of Professor Goodman, find approximate answers to these calculations:

(a) $\frac{619 - 98}{48}$ = $\frac{............ - ....}{............}$ = ... ÷ .... = ...

(b) $\frac{1034 + 1978}{297}$ = $\frac{............ + ...}{............}$ = ... ÷ .... = ...

(2 marks)

N71 Find approximate answers these questions:

(a) 2.9 × 4.1 = ... × .... = ...

(b) $\frac{5.8 + 11.9}{7.79}$ = $\frac{............ + ...}{............}$ = ... ÷ .... = ...

(2 marks)

A1 This is a notice hanging outside a holiday car hire office:

Luxury Auto Hire: All prices are per day

Family car: £20 per person, plus an additional £30

4-wheel drive: £25 per person, plus an additional £40

(a) How much would it cost for 4 people to hire a family car for 1 day?

£................................. *(1 mark)*

(b) How much would it cost for 3 people to hire a 4-wheel drive for 1 day?

£................................. *(1 mark)*

(c) How much would it cost for 2 people to hire a 4-wheel drive for 2 days?

£................................. *(1 mark)*

A2

input → ÷2 → output

(a) What is the output when the input is 2? .... *(1 mark)*

(b) What is the output when the input is 42? .... *(1 mark)*

(c) What is the input when the output is 14? .... *(1 mark)*

Algebra

NUMBER MACHINES

A3 Find the missing output.

(a)

$4 \rightarrow$ ×3 $\rightarrow$ +3 $\rightarrow$?

? = ... *(1 mark)*

(b)

$12 \rightarrow$ ×4 $\rightarrow$ ÷3 $\rightarrow$?

? = ... *(1 mark)*

(c) Find the missing input.

? $\rightarrow$ ×7 $\rightarrow$ +5 $\rightarrow$ 33

? = ... *(1 mark)*

A4

input $\rightarrow$ ÷5 $\rightarrow$ +3 $\rightarrow$ output

(a) What is the output when the input is 10? .... *(1 mark)*

(b) What is the input when the output is 7? .... *(1 mark)*

(c) By using *n* as the input, find the formula for the number machine.

.... *(1 mark)*

SUBSTITUTING VALUES

A5 Here is a formula used in engineering.

$$V = \frac{P}{3} + 5$$

SUBSTITUTING VALUES

(a) What is the value of *V* when *P* = 9?

.... *(1 mark)*

(b) What is the value of *V* when *P* = 18?

.... *(1 mark)*

SIMPLIFYING & EXPANDING EXPRESSIONS

A6 Simplify these expressions:

(a) $a + a + a + a + a$ .... 5a .... *(1 mark)*

(b) $3b - b - b + b$ .... 2b .... *(1 mark)*

(c) $4c + 4 + 3c - 2$ ...... 7c+2 .... *(1 mark)*

(d) $d + 3 + 4d - 2$ ...... 5d+1 .... *(1 mark)*

A7 Simplify these expressions:

(a) $2x + 4y + 9x - 2y$ .....l........................ *(1 mark)*

(b) $3x - 4y + 7x + 7y$ ...... 10x+3y .... *(1 mark)*

(c) $2x + 4y + 10 - x + y$ ...... x+5y+10 ...... *(1 mark)*

(d) $4x - 3x - 34 + 2y + 37$ ...... x+2y+3 ...... *(1 mark)*

A8 John has *N* books in his bag.
Don has 4 more books than John.
Fern has 2 books less than John.
Complete the table showing the number of books each person has.

Person	Number of Books
John	N
Don	N+4
Fern	N−2
Total	3N+2

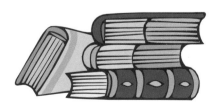

(2 marks)

35

Algebra

SIMPLIFYING & EXPANDING EXPRESSIONS

A9 Each expression in a rectangle is equal to an expression in an oval.
For example, $2(n - 1) = 2n - 2$.

Draw a line between pairs of equal expressions.

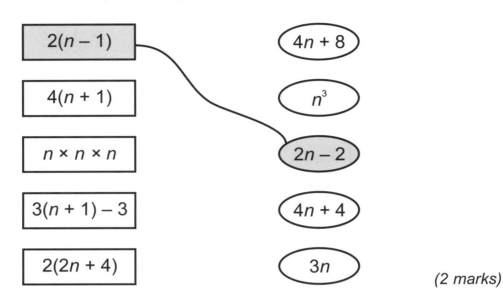

$2(n - 1)$	$4n + 8$
$4(n + 1)$	n^3
$n \times n \times n$	$2n - 2$
$3(n + 1) - 3$	$4n + 4$
$2(2n + 4)$	$3n$

(2 marks)

SOLVING EQUATIONS

A10 Find the missing number.

(a) $\boxed{} + 5 = 15$ (b) $3 \times \boxed{} + 8 = 20$ (c) $\boxed{} \div 2 - 3 = 1$

(3 marks)

A11 Brenda has won this year's super trophy.

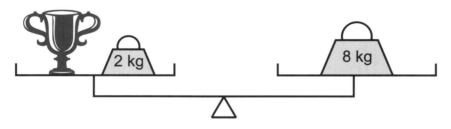

How much does Brenda's trophy weigh?

.... kg *(1 mark)*

A12 Find the value of x in each of these.

(a) $5x = 15$

$x =$ .... *(1 mark)*

(b) $x + 2 = 4$

$x =$ .... *(1 mark)*

(c) $3x - 2 = 4$

$x =$ .... *(1 mark)*

A13 Solve these equations

(a) $2y + 3 = 23$

$y =$ .... *(1 mark)*

(b) $8y = 4y + 16$

$y =$ .... *(1 mark)*

A14 Jerome thinks of a number, n.
Jerome multiplies his number by 2 and then adds 5 to get the answer 17.

(a) Fill in the gaps in this linear equation for n.

$$\boxed{} \times n + \boxed{} = \boxed{}$$ *(1 mark)*

(b) Solve the linear equation to find Jerome's number, n.

$n =$ .... *(1 mark)*

A15 Describe how to obtain the next term in each of these number patterns:

(a) 2, 4, 6, 8, 10, 12

(1 mark)

(b) 1, 2, 4, 8, 16, 22

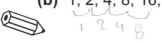

(1 mark)

37

Algebra

(c) 5, 6, 8, 11, 15,...19

(1 mark)

A16 Some number patterns start: 1, 3,...

Write down the next 2 terms in each of these patterns:

(a) 1, 3, 5, [7], [9],...

(b) 1, 3, 6, [11], [20],...

(c) 1, 3, 9, [19], [33],...

(3 marks)

A17 Find the next 3 terms in this pattern.

1, 4, 9, 16, 25, [36], [49], [64],...

(1 mark)

A18 Draw the next picture in each of these patterns.

(a)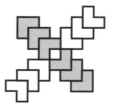

(1 mark)

(b)

(1 mark)

(c)

(1 mark)

38

A19 Find the *n*th term of each of these number patterns.

(a) 1, 2, 3, 4, 5,...

..........6, 7, 8, 9.............. *(1 mark)*

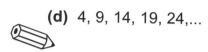

(b) 3, 6, 9, 12, 15,...

..........18, 21, 24, 27.... *(1 mark)*

(c) 2, 5, 8, 11, 14,...

..........17, 20, 23, 26..... *(1 mark)*

(d) 4, 9, 14, 19, 24,...

....29, 34, 39, 44..... *(1 mark)*

A20 Write down the coordinates of each point.

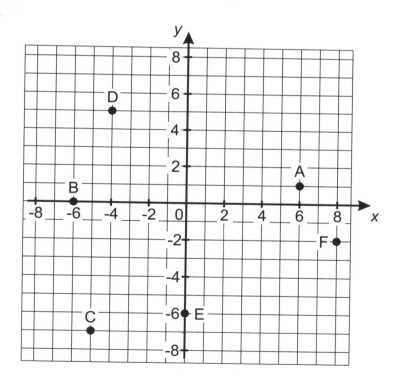

A (...6... , ...1...) B (..-6.... , ...0...) C (...-5... , ..-7....)

D (..-5... , ...4...) E (...0.... , ..-6...) F (...8.... , ..-2....)

(3 marks)

Algebra

A21 The vertices of a shape have the coordinates:

(1,1), (1, 5), (5, 5), (5,1)

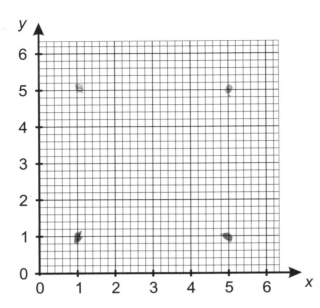

(a) Draw the shape on the graph paper provided.

(2 marks)

(b) What kind of shape have you drawn?

................................Square..........................✓........ *(1 mark)*

A22 The vertices of a shape have coordinates (-4,-1), (-2,2), (4,2) and (2,-1).

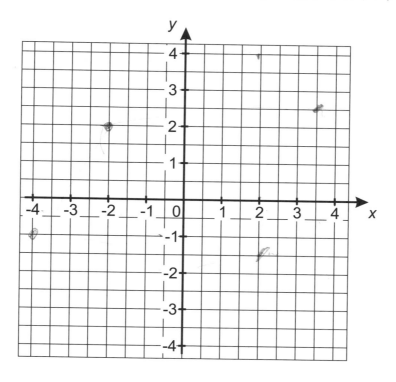

(a) Plot the points, joining them in order.

(2 marks)

(b) What shape have you drawn?

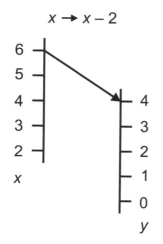

.... Rhombas parelleb ghram .... *(1 mark)*

A23 By drawing arrows, complete each mapping diagram.

$x \rightarrow x - 2$

$x \rightarrow 2x$

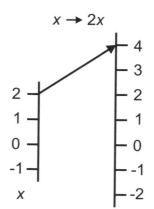

(2 marks)

Algebra

A24 (a) Complete this mapping diagram.

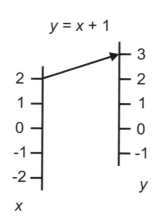

$y = x + 1$

(1 mark)

(b) List the coordinates for the mapping.

(......... , ...), (......... , ...), (......... , ...),

(......... , ...), (......... , ...)

(1 mark)

(c) Plot the points from **(b)** on these axes.
Join the points to make a graph.

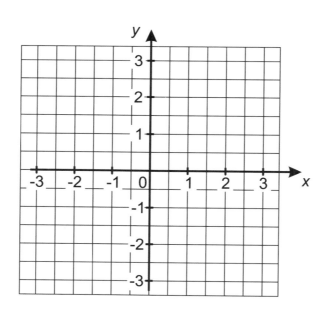

(2 marks)

42

A25 Find the gradient of each of these lines.

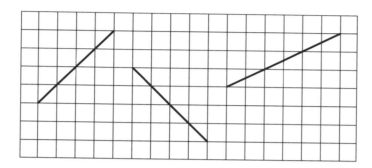

....

(3 marks)

A26 Draw and label lines with gradients of:

(a) 2

(b) -2

(c) -0.5

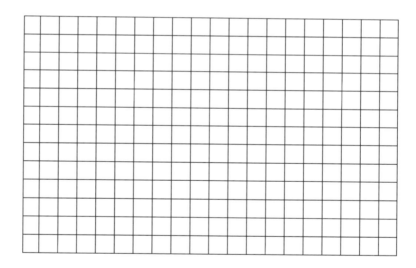

(3 marks)

A27 (a) Complete this table of values for the line $y = 2x$.

x	0	1	2	3
$y = 2x$				

(2 marks)

Algebra

(b) Plot the points and join them together to make a graph.

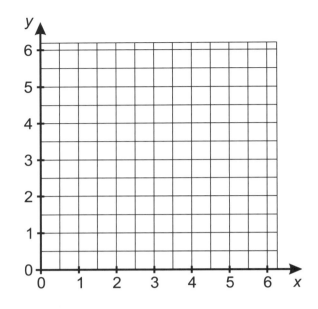

(2 marks)

A28 Match these equations to their graphs:

$$y = x \qquad y = -x \qquad y = 3 \qquad x = 3$$

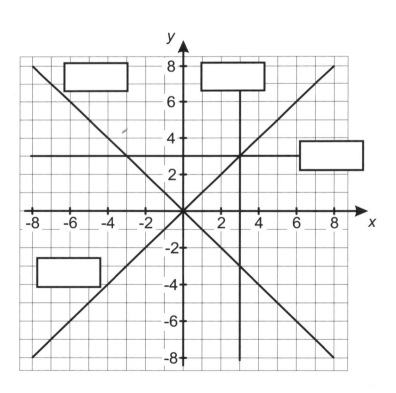

(2 marks)

A29

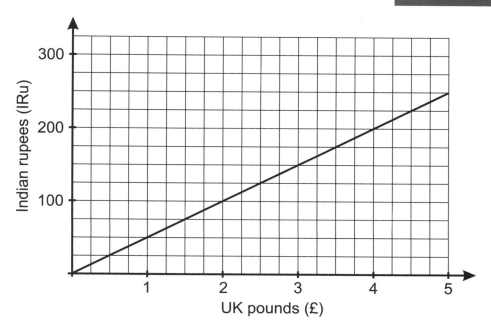

Use the conversion graph to find

(a) £4 in Indian rupees,

IRu ....200............ *(1 mark)* ✓

(b) IRu175 in UK pounds.

£...........3.50.................. *(1 mark)* ✓

Algebra

A30 The distance-time graph below shows Pippa's journey from her home (H) to her local sports centre (S).

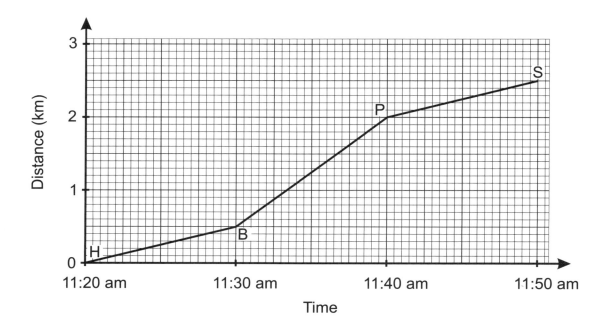

(a) What is the distance from Pippa's home (H) to the sports centre (S)?

.............2.5............. km *(1 mark)*

(b) How long does it take Pippa to travel from the bus stop (B) to the post office (P)?

.............10............. minutes *(1 mark)*

(c) For which part of the journey is Pippa travelling the fastest?

.............B........ to ...P......... *(1 mark)*

A31 Ingid has started to solve the equation $4x^2 = 25$ by trial and improvement. Complete her solution, giving your answer to 1 decimal place.

First estimate is $x = 3$.
If $x = 3$, then $4x^2 = 4 \times 3^2 = 4 \times 9 = 36$, which is too big.
So try a smaller x.

Try x = ...

x = ...*(3 marks)*

Shape, Space & Measures

MEASURING SCALES

S1 **(a)** John is trying to measure the length of his eraser.

(i) How long is his eraser?

.... cm *(1 mark)*

(ii) Peter has an eraser that is 3.5 cm long.
Draw Peter's eraser in the space below the ruler. *(1 mark)*

(b) Using your ruler, measure exactly the length of the line below.

.... cm *(1 mark)*

S2 This is the dial on a weighing machine.

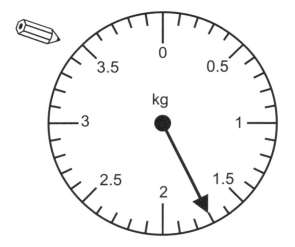

(a) Write down the weight that the dial is displaying.

.... kg *(1 mark)*

(b) On the dial, draw the new position of the pointer if a further 1.3 kg is added to the machine. *(2 marks)*

S3 Beth is at the airport. A clock above the departures desk shows that it is 6:30pm.

(a) How would this time be written on a 24-hour digital clock? Write your answer in the box below.

18 : 30

(1 mark)

(b) Beth's flight leaves 45 minutes later. Draw hands on the blank clockface to show the time that Beth's flight takes off.

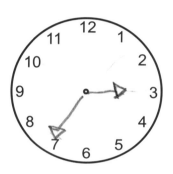

(1 mark)

S4 Karl is travelling through Ohio, USA. He is going to take the train from Cleveland to Cincinnati. Here is the timetable:

Cleveland	11:02	13:02	15:02
Columbus	12:23	14:23	16:23
Dayton	13:19	15:19	17:19
Cincinnati	14:17	16:17	18:17

(a) What is the earliest time he can leave Cleveland?

..........11:02.............. *(1 mark)*

(b) How long will his journey take?

..........3.......... hours ....11............ minutes *(1 mark)*

Shape, Space & Measures

S5 **(a)** How many lines of symmetry do each of these signs have?

Sign 1

.... lines of symmetry

Sign 2

.... lines of symmetry

Sign 3

.... lines of symmetry

Sign 4

.... lines of symmetry

(4 marks)

(b) Complete these statements.

The order of rotational symmetry of sign 1 is ....

The order of rotational symmetry of sign 2 is ....

The order of rotational symmetry of sign 3 is ....

The order of rotational symmetry of sign 4 is ....

(4 marks)

S6 **(a)** The dotted lines are lines of symmetry.
Complete each shape so that it is symmetrical.

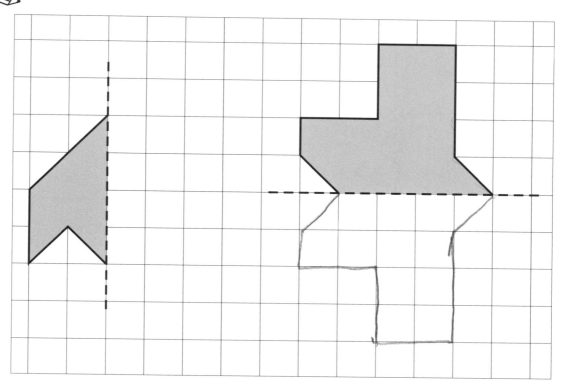

(2 marks)

(b) This shape has two lines of symmetry. Complete the shape.

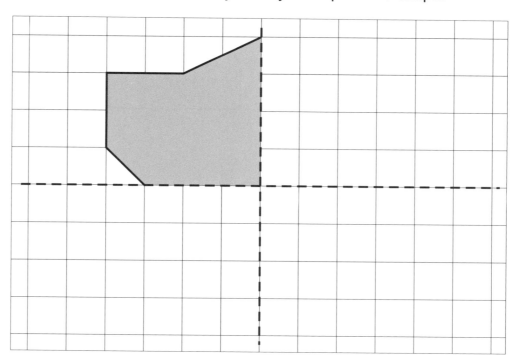

(2 marks)

Shape, Space & Measures

S7 Complete this table.

Name	Sketch	Number of lines of symmetry	Order of rotational symmetry
equilateral triangle		3	
rectangle			
regular hexagon			

(5 marks)

S8 Here is a cuboid.

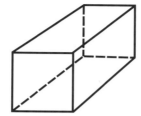

Which of these nets could *not* be folded to make a cuboid?

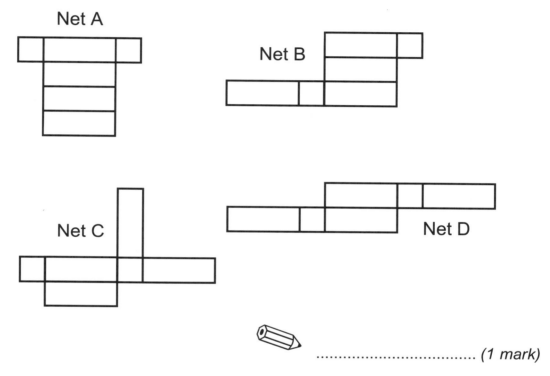

Net A

Net B

Net C

Net D

.... *(1 mark)*

S9 What is the mathematical name for the shapes that these nets will make when folded?

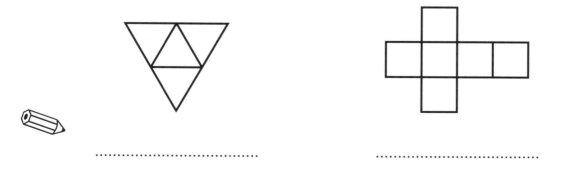

....

(2 marks)

Shape, Space & Measures

S10 Draw a net for this triangular prism.

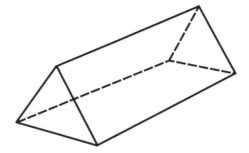

(2 marks)

S11 This map shows some of the landmarks near Cassy's house.

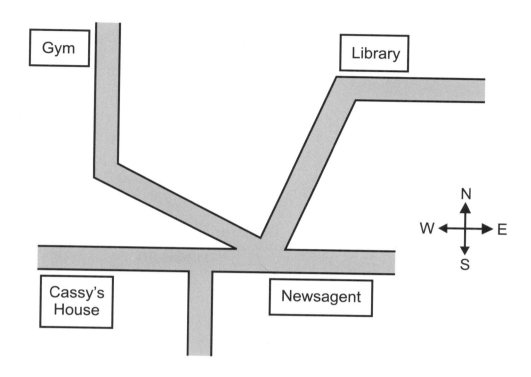

(a) Which landmark is west of the library?

.......Gym.. *(1 mark)*

(b) In which direction does Cassy need to travel from her house to get to the newsagent?

.......East.. *(1 mark)*

(c) What is the direction of the gym from the newsagent?

.......North west... *(1 mark)*

Shape, Space & Measures

QUADRILATERALS

S12 (a) Link each name to its shape with a line.

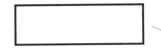

Parallelogram

Rectangle

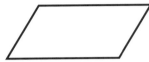

Rhombus

Kite

Square

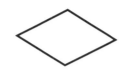

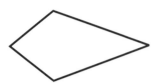

Trapezium

(3 marks)

(b) Which of these shapes does *not* have any parallel sides?

.... *(1 mark)*

POLYGONS

S13 (a) What do the angles in a triangle add up to?

...................................° *(1 mark)*

(b) Without measuring, work out the size of the missing angle in this triangle.

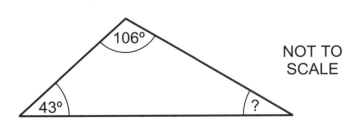

NOT TO SCALE

? = ...° *(2 marks)*

56

Shape, Space & Measures

S14 (a) What do the angles in a quadrilateral add up to?

..................................° *(1 mark)*

(b) Without measuring, work out the size of the missing angle in this quadrilateral.

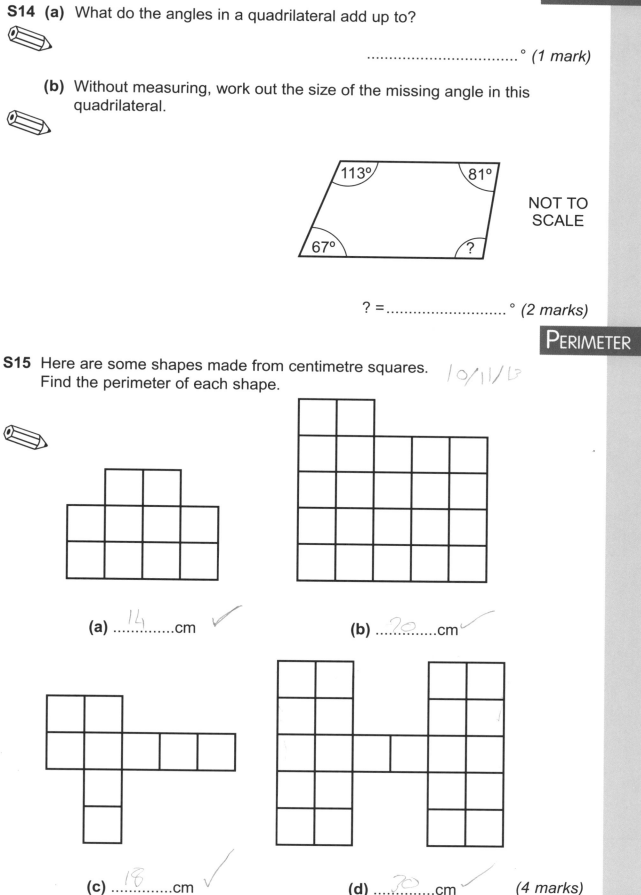

NOT TO SCALE

? =..........................° *(2 marks)*

S15 Here are some shapes made from centimetre squares. Find the perimeter of each shape.

10/11/13

(a) .....14.......cm ✓

(b) .....20.......cm ✓

(c) .....18.......cm ✓

(d) .....20.......cm ✓ *(4 marks)*

57

10/11/13

PERIMETER

S16 By first working out the length of any missing sides, work out the perimeter of these shapes.

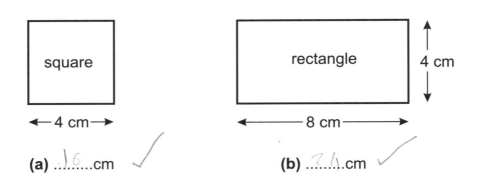

square

←4 cm→

rectangle

4 cm

←8 cm→

(a) ..16...cm ✓

(b) ..24...cm ✓

NOT TO SCALE

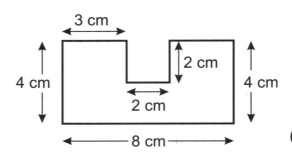

3 cm

4 cm

2 cm

2 cm

4 cm

←8 cm→

(c) ..28...cm ✓

(3 marks)

S17 Using a suitable formula, calculate the circumference of these circles. Show your working and take π as 3.14, or use the π button on your calculator.

(a)

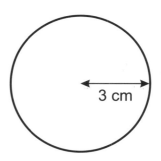

3 cm

..18.8.......... cm *(2 marks)* ✗

16/11/13

(b)

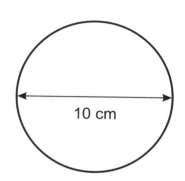

10 cm

.................31.4.. cm *(2 marks)* ✓

S18 These shapes are made from centimetre squares.
Find the area of each shape.

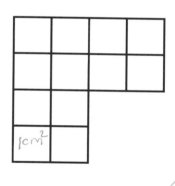

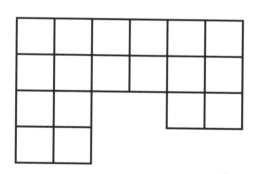

1cm²

(a) ......12......cm² ✓

(b) ......18....cm² ✓

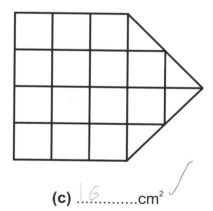

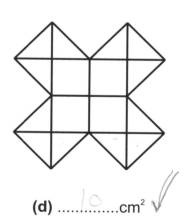

(c) ...16.........cm² ✓

(d) ......10....cm² ✓

(4 marks)

59

lo/11/8

S19 Calculate the area of these two rectangles.

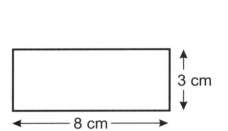

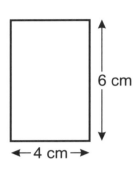

NOT TO SCALE

(a) area = ...2 4.... cm² ✓   **(b)** area = ...2 4.... cm² ✓

(2 marks)

S20 Calculate the area of these two triangles.

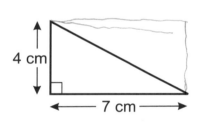

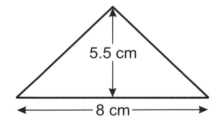

NOT TO SCALE

(a) area = ...1 4... cm² ✓   **(b)** area = ...2 2.. cm² ✓

(2 marks)

S21 Using suitable formulae, calculate the area of the parallelogram and the trapezium.

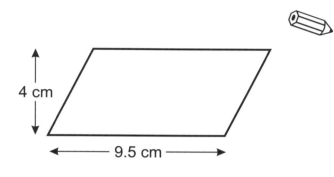

4 cm

9.5 cm

NOT TO SCALE

(a) area = ... cm²

(2 marks)

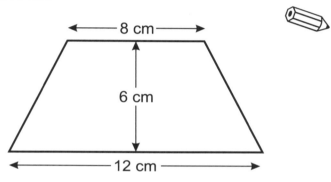

8 cm

6 cm

12 cm

(b) area = ... cm²

(2 marks)

S22 Calculate, using the correct formula, the area of these circles. Take π as 3.14 or use the π button on your calculator.

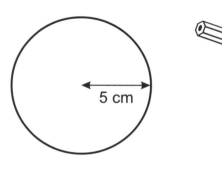

5 cm

(a) area = ... cm²

(2 marks)

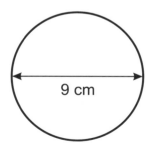

9 cm

(b) area = ... cm²

(2 marks)

NOT TO SCALE

Shape, Space & Measures

VOLUME

S23 This is a cube with side 1 cm.
It has a volume of 1 cm³.

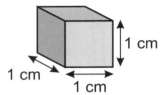

(a) Find the volume of the shape below.

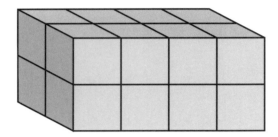

.... cm³ *(1 mark)*

(b) What is the volume of this shape?

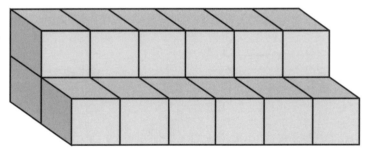

.... cm³ *(1 mark)*

S24 (a) In terms of its height, width and length, what is the formula for the volume of a cuboid?

Volume of a cuboid = ... *(1 mark)*

(b) Work out the volume of this box.

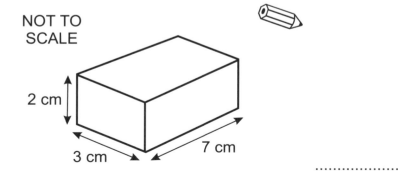

NOT TO SCALE

2 cm

3 cm   7 cm

.... cm³ *(1 mark)*

S25 What is the volume of a box with dimensions 5 cm by 8.5 cm by 6 cm?

.... cm³ *(1 mark)*

S26 Measure each of these angles with a protractor or angle measurer.

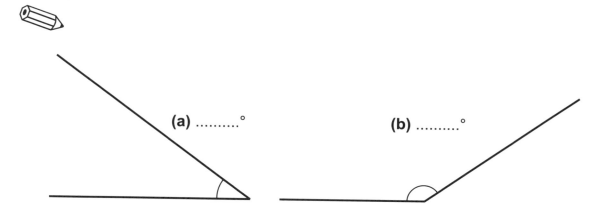

(a) ....°   **(b)** ....°

(2 marks)

(c) Is the angle in part **(a)** acute, obtuse or reflex?

.... *(1 mark)*

(d) Is the angle in part **(b)** acute, obtuse or reflex?

.... *(1 mark)*

(e) Draw an example of a reflex angle.

(1 mark)

Shape, Space & Measures

ANGLES

S27 (a) How many degrees are there in a right angle?

.................................° *(1 mark)*

(b) How many degrees are there in a half turn?

.................................° *(1 mark)*

(c) How many degrees are there in a full turn?

.................................° *(1 mark)*

S28 Work out the size of the missing angles.

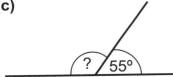

(a)

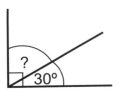

? = ...°

(b)

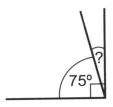

? = ...°

(c)

? = ...°

(d)

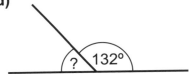

? = ...°

(e)

310°

? = ...°

(f)

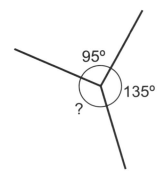

95°

135°

?

? = ...°   *(6 marks)*

64

S29 Here is a rough sketch of a model boat.

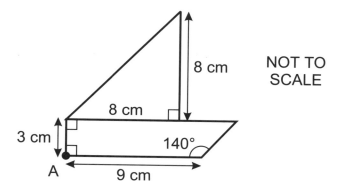

By starting at point A, make an accurate drawing of the model boat.

A ●

Shape, Space & Measures

METRIC & IMPERIAL UNITS

S30 (a) What is 5.2 m in centimetres?

..........520.......................... cm *(1 mark)*

(b) How many millimetres are in 23 cm?

..........230.......................... mm *(1 mark)*

(c) Write 3200 mm in metres.

..........3·2.......................... m *(1 mark)*

S31 (a) How many grams are in 0.8 kg?

..........800.......................... g *(1 mark)*

(b) Write 2400 g in kilograms.

..........2.4.......................... kg *(1 mark)*

S32 (a) How many millilitres are in 1.2 litres?

..........1200.......................... ml *(1 mark)*

(b) Write 3000 ml in litres.

..........3.0.......................... litres *(1 mark)*

S33 (a) Katie needs 4 oz of flour for a recipe.
How many grams of flour is this?

.... g *(1 mark)*

(b) Katie also needs 0.75 litres of milk for this recipe.
How many pints of milk does she need?

.... pints *(1 mark)*

S34 (a) Gareth ran 10 km on Saturday.
How many miles is this?

..............·010..........miles *(1 mark)*

(b) Gareth is 6 ft tall.
How tall is Gareth in metres?

.... m *(1 mark)*

S35 Susan is standing next to an advertising billboard.

Ice Cream Cones

Available in Vanilla flavour

(a) Estimate the height of the billboard in metres.

.... m *(1 mark)*

(b) Estimate the width of the billboard in metres.

.... m *(1 mark)*

Shape, Space & Measures

ISOMETRIC DRAWINGS

S36 Draw each shape after it has been turned upside down.
The drawings have been started for you.

(a)

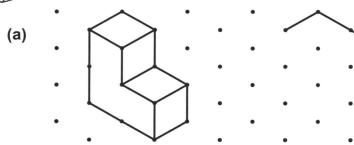

(b)

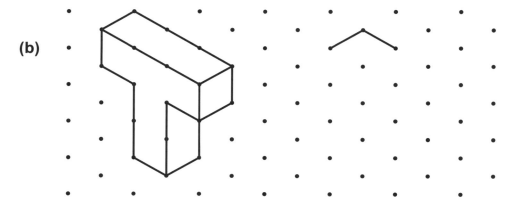

(2 marks)

Here are the front, side and top elevations of shape **(a)**.

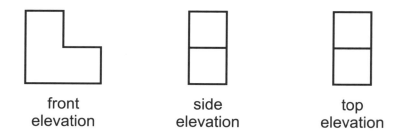

front
elevation

side
elevation

top
elevation

(c) Sketch the front, side and top elevations of shape **(b)**.

front
elevation

side
elevation

top
elevation

(2 marks)

S37 This LOGO program was used to draw the rectangle:

FORWARD 10
LEFT TURN 90
FORWARD 6
LEFT TURN 90
FORWARD 10
LEFT TURN 90
FORWARD 6
LEFT TURN 90

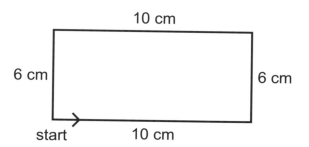

(a) Follow the LOGO program below to draw another shape.

FORWARD 5
LEFT TURN 60
FORWARD 4
LEFT TURN 120
FORWARD 5
LEFT TURN 60
FORWARD 4
LEFT TURN 120

(2 marks)

(b) What is the mathematical name of the shape you have drawn?

.... *(1 mark)*

The LOGO program used to draw the rectangle could have been written as:

REPEAT 2 [FORWARD 10, LEFT TURN 90, FORWARD 6, LEFT TURN 90]

(c) Using the REPEAT command, write the LOGO program in part **(a)** a different way.

(1 mark)

Shape, Space & Measures

TRANSFORMATIONS

S38 Draw an enlargement of shape LMNOPQ with scale factor 3.

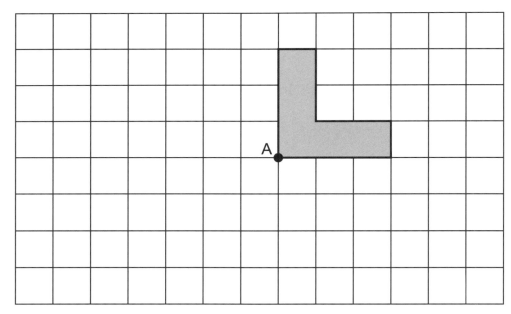

(2 marks)

S39

(a) Rotate the L shape 90° clockwise about the point A.   *(1 mark)*

(b) Rotate the L shape 180° clockwise about the point A.   *(1 mark)*

S40 Reflect each shape in the line $x = 3$.

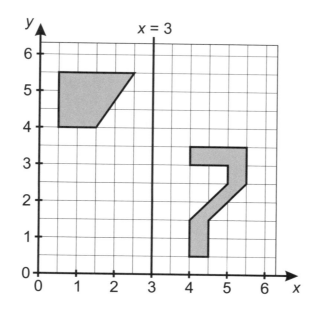

(2 marks)

S41 Some of these angles are the same.

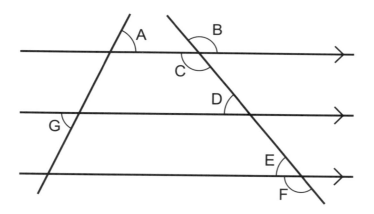

Complete these statements:

(a) Angle A is the same size as angle ....   *(1 mark)*

(b) Angle D is the same size as angle ....   *(1 mark)*

(c) Angle C is the same size as angle .... and angle ....   *(1 mark)*

(d) The sum of angle C and angle D is ....°   *(1 mark)*

Shape, Space & Measures

S42 The diagram below shows part of a tessellation that uses a certain type of quadrilateral.

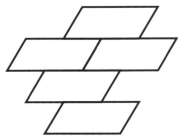

(a) What is the mathematical name given to the quadrilateral used in the tessellation?

.... *(1 mark)*

(b) Continue the tessellation, in the same way, on the grid below.
Add at least four more quadrilaterals.

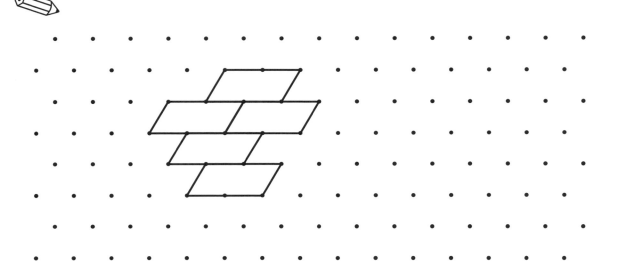

(1 mark)

The quadrilaterals can also tessellate in different ways.

(c) Draw a different tessellation pattern using the quadrilaterals on the grid below.

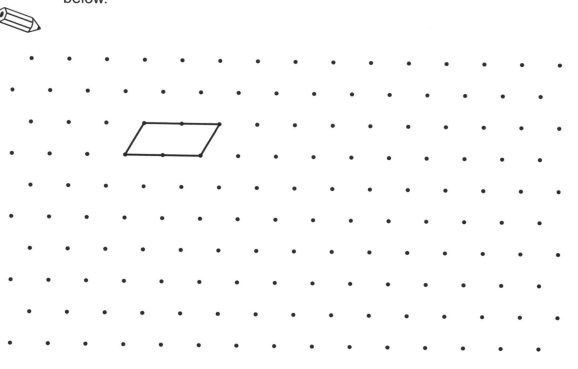

(1 mark)

S43 Each of these shapes is congruent to one other shape.

Draw loops around each congruent pair.

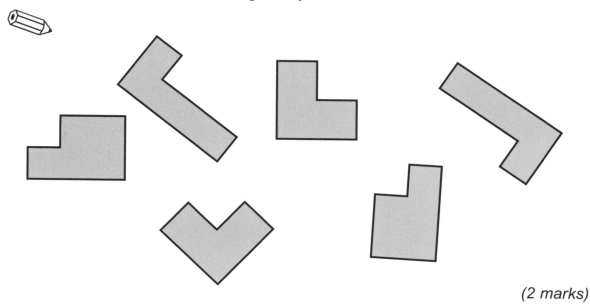

(2 marks)

Handling Data

FREQUENCY DIAGRAMS

H1 Tariq heard on the radio that people need to eat 5 portions of fruit or vegetables each day.
To investigate this, Tariq carried out a survey of how many portions of fruit or vegetables a group of people ate during one week.

7	12	8	8	18	14	8	20	13
6	5	17	10	13	1	25	9	8

(a) Complete the tally/frequency table.

Number of portions in one week	1 to 5	6 to 10	11 to 15	16 to 20	21 to 25
Tally	|||	HHT||	/|||	|||		
Frequency	3	7	4	3	1

(2 marks)

(b) How many people took part in Tariq's survey?

..............18.............. *(1 mark)*

(c) Do the people in Tariq's survey eat more or less fruit or vegetables than the radio program recommended?

(1 mark)

74

Handling Data

H2 Joanne is a striker for a non-league football team. She has kept a record of the number of goals she scored in the first 14 matches of the season.

3   0   2   0   2   3   0   1   0   2   3   0   3   2

(a) Find the modal number of goals that Joanne scored in the first 14 matches.

........................0........................ (2 marks)

(b) Do you think that Joanne's modal score would help her get a transfer to a better football club? Explain.

Rosent Score any goals

(1 mark)

H3 The weights of 9 basketball players are shown below.

85 kg, 91 kg, 84 kg, 94 kg, 84 kg, 88 kg, 93 kg, 84 kg, 93 kg

(a) By putting the weights in order, find the median weight.

........88.............. kg (2 marks)

(b) Find the mode of their weights.   ....84................ kg (1 mark)

(c) Which of the averages is NOT a good indicator of the basketball players' average weight? Why? *Lowest weight*

(1 mark)

75

Handling Data

H4 What is the mean of the following numbers?

3, 5, 4, 6, 1, 5

.................4................. *(2 marks)*

H5 Ruud measures the diameters of some oranges.
The diameters, in mm, are:

80, 82, 82, 83, 85, 89, 91, 92, 92, 94

(a) What is the range of the diameters of the oranges?

.........14............... mm *(1 mark)*

(b) What is the mean diameter of the oranges?

.................8.7....... mm *(3 marks)*

76

H6 The bar chart shows the favourite ice cream flavours of people in a class.

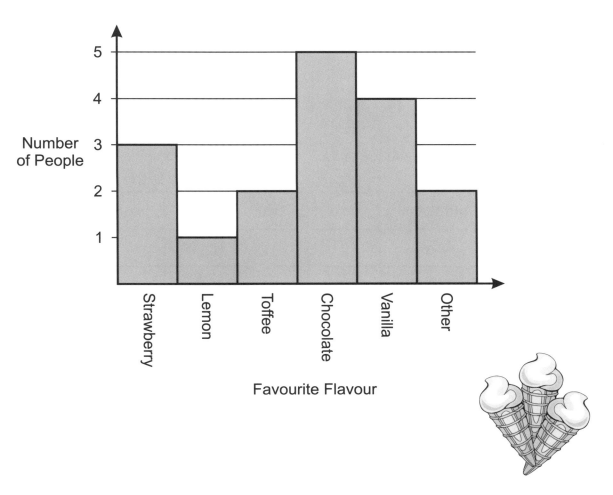

(a) How many people chose toffee as their favourite flavour?

.............2.................... *(1 mark)*

(b) How many people are in the class?

.............17.................... *(1 mark)*

Handling Data

H7 Carrie carried out a survey in her street.
She recorded which houses had one bedroom (O), two bedrooms (Tw), three bedrooms (Th) or more than three bedrooms (M).
The raw data is shown below.

Tw   Th   Tw   M   Ø   Th   Tw   Ø   Th   Tw   Ø

M   Th   Ø   Tw   Tw   Tw   Ø   Th   M   Th   Ø

(a) Complete the frequency table.

Bedrooms	One	Two	Three	More
Tally	ⅢⅠ	ⅢⅢⅠⅠ	ⅢⅠ	ⅠⅠⅠ
Frequency	6	7	6	3

(2 marks)

(b) Complete the bar chart to illustrate Carrie's data.

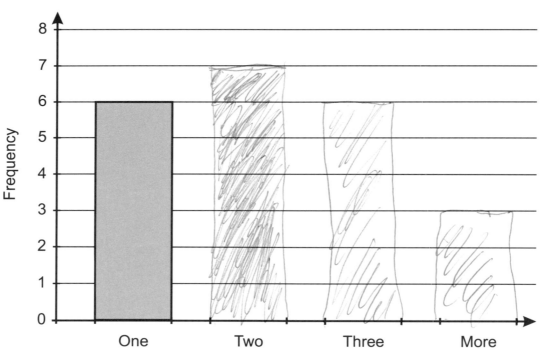

Number of Bedrooms

(2 marks)

H8   The graph shows the temperature in Donald's greenhouse at midday every day of one week.

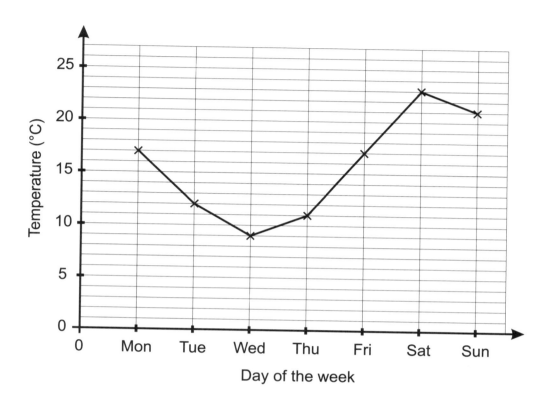

(a)   How hot was it at midday on Tuesday?

.....................12.............. °C *(1 mark)*

(b)   On which day was it coldest at midday?

.........Wednesday.......... *(1 mark)*

(c)   Which 2 days had the same temperature at midday?

.......Monday............. and ......Friday................. *(1 mark)*

If the temperature in the greenhouse is over 22°C at midday then Donald waters his plants in the evening.

(d)   On which day did Donald water his plants in the evening?

.............Saturday.......... *(1 mark)*

Handling Data

LINE GRAPHS

H9 The heights of some flowers are displayed in the table below.

Height (cm)	Frequency
5	3
10	7
15	9
20	5
25	4

Show these heights in a line graph.

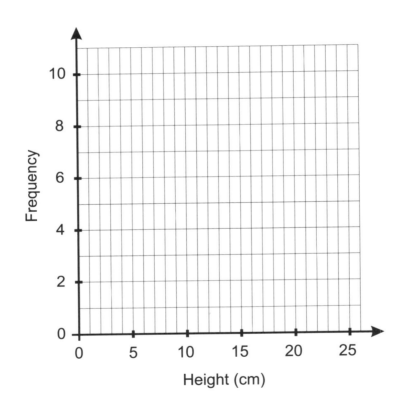

(2 marks)

H10 A shop sells watch straps in 5 different colours.
The pie chart shows the colour distribution of 800 watch straps sold.

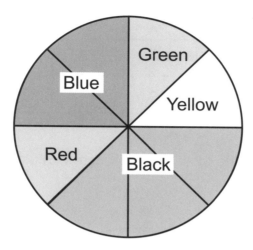

(a) What fraction of the watch straps sold were yellow?

.... $\frac{1}{8}$ .... *(1 mark)*

(b) How many yellow watch straps were sold?

.... 300 .... *(1 mark)*

(c) How many of the watch straps sold were black?

.... *(2 marks)*

Handling Data

H11 On a certain day last year, a bicycle factory produced 180 mountain bikes.
The table below shows the colours of the bikes.

Colour	White	Red	Blue	Grey	Total
Number	88	22	18	52	180
Angle	176	44	36	104	360°

(a) By first completing the table above, construct a pie chart in the circle below.

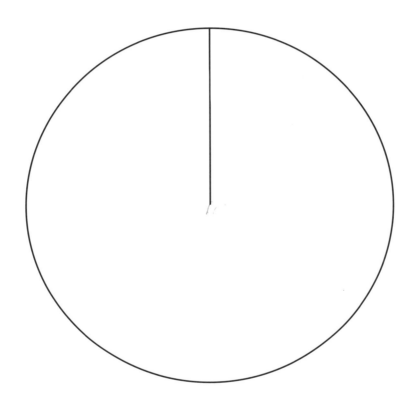

(5 marks)

(b) What fraction of the mountain bikes were blue?
Write your fraction in its lowest terms.

.................1/5................. *(2 marks)*

H12 Shabiza is investigating how the extension of a spring varies with mass.

 5

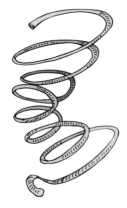

The scatter graph below shows her results.

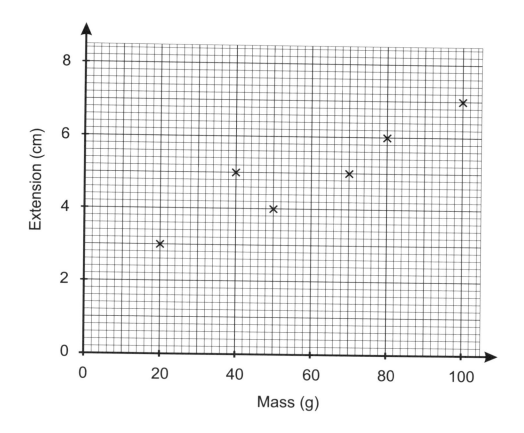

Make a rough estimate of the extension if a 60 g mass is hung from the spring.

........................5...... cm *(2 marks)*

Handling Data

H13 This scatter graph shows the marks achieved by eight trainee secretaries in their typing and shorthand tests. The marks are given as percentages.

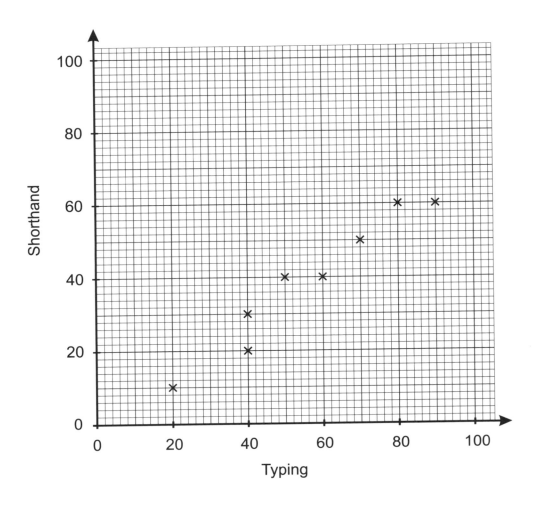

(a) Describe what the diagram tells you.

(1 mark)

David had to miss the shorthand test, due to illness, having scored 50% in the typing test.

(b) What mark do you think David would have scored in the shorthand test?

.... % *(2 marks)*

84

H14

impossible	very unlikely	unlikely
evens	likely	very likely	certain

Use one of these words or phrases to complete each statement.

(a) It is ..Very.unlikely..................
that 12 people in your class share the same birthday. *(1 mark)*

(b) It is ...cartaly...
that the next bus you catch will have a driver. *(1 mark)*

(c) It is ...even...
that the next baby to be born in London is a boy. *(1 mark)*

H15 This fair spinner is spun.

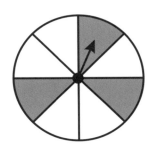

(a) **(i)** Is it more likely to land on grey or white?

....White........... *(1 mark)* ✓

(ii) Give a reason for your answer.

More white than grey

(1 mark)

(b) Mark the probability line below with a cross to show the probability that the spinner will land on grey.

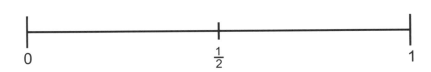

0   ½   1

(1 mark)

Handling Data

H16 A bag contains 7 red beads and 8 blue beads.
A bead is taken from the bag at random.
Find the probability that the bead taken is

(a) red,

.... $\frac{7}{15}$ .... *(1 mark)*

(b) not red.

.... $\frac{8}{15}$ .... *(1 mark)*

H17 In a game, a fair coin is tossed and a fair 6-sided dice rolled.
A head is worth 2 and a tail is worth 3.
This score is added to the number on the dice.

(a) Complete the table to show all possible scores.

		DICE					
+		1	2	3	4	5	6
C O I N	2	3	4	5			
	3	4					

(1 mark)

(b) What is the probability that the score is

(i) 5? .... $\frac{1}{6}$ .... *(1 mark)*

(ii) greater than 6? .... $\frac{5}{12}$ .... *(1 mark)*

(iii) 2? .... 0 .... *(1 mark)*

Mental Mathematics Questions

1. Photocopy or detach the answer sheet on page 96 of this book.
2. Ask a friend or adult to read out the questions slowly. They should read each question twice and then pause for the number of seconds allowed for answering.
3. Work out the answers in your head and write them in the spaces provided on the answer sheet. For some of the questions important information is written down for you on the answer sheet.

5 Seconds

M1 Divide fifty-six by seven.
M2 Write the number three thousand, two hundred and six in figures.
M3 How many centimetres are there in two metres?
M4 Multiply three by six and then subtract four.
M5 How many degrees are there in a right angle?
M6 What is fifty-two point seven multiplied by one hundred?
M7 Look at the equation on your answer sheet. What is the value of p ?

10 Seconds

M8 How much would you pay for three cards that cost two pounds and twenty pence each?
M9 An equilateral triangle has sides of length seven centimetres.
What is the perimeter of the triangle?
M10 How many minutes are there in four hours?
M11 The bar chart on your answer sheet shows the colours of some teacher's cars. There are twelve cars of a certain colour. Which colour is that?
M12 What is three quarters minus a half?
M13 Karl watered twenty-three per cent of his garden.
What percentage of his garden did he not water?
M14 A digital camera cost forty pounds. The price goes up by ten per cent.
What is the new price of the digital camera?
M15 Look at the expression on your answer sheet. Write the expression as simply as possible.
M16 Look at the rectangle and square on your answer sheet.
How many of the rectangles would fit into the square?
M17 Look at the equation on your answer sheet. What is the value of b ?
M18 A car started its journey at three thirty-five in the afternoon; it arrived at four fifteen the same afternoon. How long did the journey take?
M19 Look at the diagram on your answer sheet. What size is the missing angle?
M20 The temperature was two degrees Celsius, before it dropped by twelve degrees.
What is the new temperature?
M21 Donald counted the number of red and blue cars that passed his house one afternoon. His tallies are shown on your answer sheet. How many red and blue cars did he count in total?

15 Seconds

M22 Look at the numbers on your answer sheet. Which is the largest number?
M23 How many lines of symmetry does the shape on your answer sheet have?
M24 Look at the nets on your answer sheet. Which of them would not fold to make a cube?
M25 Use the calculation on your answer sheet to work out the answer to two hundred and twenty-four divided by eight.
M26 A book costs one pound ninety-nine. Dave bought three books.
How much change did he get from eight pounds?
M27 Look at the spinner on your answer sheet.
What is the probability of the spinner landing on grey?
M28 What is the next prime number after thirteen?
M29 Imagine a solid cylinder, standing on a circular end. Cut the cylinder in half, from top to bottom. What is the shape of the vertical face made by the cut?
M30 The pie chart shows the colours of seventy-five flowers in a garden.
How many flowers are yellow?

Answers

NUMBER

N1 264

N2 Five hundred and fifty-five, seventeen, five thousand and eight, one hundred and fifty-nine

N3 9, 15, 27, 64, 99, 101

N4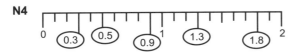

N5 10.25, 11.25, 15.21, 20.51

N6 19.91

N7 1.125, 1.5, 11.25, 12

N8 (a) 861   (b) 168

N9 (a) £97.52   (b) £25.79

N10 24 − 5 = 19, 37 + 41 = 78, 137 − 73 = 64

N11 (a) 76 parcels   (b) 27 parcels

N12 14.4 − 8.5 = 5.9 cm

N13 (a) 17.4 m   (b) 3.5 m

N14

×	1	3	5
2	2	6	10
4	4	12	20
8	8	24	40

×	3	7	9
4	12	28	36
7	21	49	63
10	30	70	90

N15 (a) 48 jars   (b) 144 jars

N16 84 ÷ 6 = 14 bushes

N17 (a) Harvey has multiplied 40 by 7. He should have divided by 7.

     (b) 6 boxes   (c) 2 tubs

N18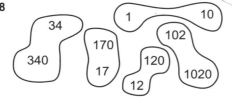

N19 (a) 1600   (b) 12 000   (c) 10   (d) 100

N20 (a) 50   (b) 56   (c) 100   (d) 100

N21 (a) 7   (b) 33

N22 (a) £5488   (b) £928

N23 (a) £45   (b) £720   (c) 502

N24 (a) £1.40   (b) £3.60   (c) 71

N25 (a) £155   (b) £40

N26 (a) A shirt or a belt.

     (b) The shirt and the belt, leaving 2p change.

N27 (a) £1.98, £2.03 (to nearest penny)

     (b) 200 g   (c) 100 g

N28 $\frac{1}{3}$

N30 (a) $\frac{2}{3}$ (b) $\frac{1}{3}$

N31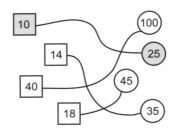

N32 (a) 105   (b) 35

N33 $\frac{4}{6}, \frac{12}{18}, \frac{6}{9}, \frac{20}{30}$

N34 (a) $\frac{1}{5} + \frac{2}{10} = \frac{3}{15}$ is wrong

     (b) $\frac{1}{5} + \frac{2}{10} = \frac{1}{5} + \frac{1}{5} = \frac{2}{5}$

N35 (a) $\frac{1}{3}$ (b) $\frac{2}{3}$

N36 (a) 0.9   (b) 0.5   (c) 0.75   (d) 0.2

N37 2 parts, 2 parts and 6 parts shaded

N38 (a) 1.43   (b) 4.88   (c) 9.5   (d) 5.25

N39 (a) 47.64   (b) 73.37   (c) 28.61   (d) 9.09

N40 (a) 100   (b) 100   (c) 100   (d) 10

N41 42.54

N42 13.4

N43 (a) 30.6   (b) 31.26   (c) 7.33

     (d) 2.61   (e) 10   (f) 100

N44 (a) 67.2   (b) 134.4   (c) 1344

N45 (a)

N46

Fraction	Decimal	Percentage
$\frac{1}{10}$	0.1	10%
$\frac{1}{5}$	0.2	20%
$\frac{1}{4}$	0.25	25%
$\frac{1}{2}$	0.5	50%
$\frac{3}{4}$	0.75	75%
$\frac{9}{10}$	0.9	90%

N47 (a) £5   (b) £0.70   (c) £45

     (d) £0.60   (e) £6

N48

Subject	Percentage
Maths	60%
English	55%
Science	30%
Art	60%
French	65%
Information Technology	55%

N49 **(a)** £72 **(b)** £128 **(c)** £176

(d) £59.40 **(e)** 15%

N50

Fraction	Decimal	Percentage
$\frac{1}{20}$	0.05	5%
$\frac{7}{20}$	0.35	35%
$\frac{3}{8}$	0.375	37.5%
$\frac{5}{8}$	0.625	62.5%
$\frac{16}{25}$	0.64	64%
$\frac{37}{50}$	0.74	74%

N51 **(a)** 1, 4, 9, 16, 25 **(b)** 2, 3, 5, 7, 11

N52 **(a)** 12, 20 **(b)** 2, 3, 12 **(c)** 2, 3, 17

N53 **(a) & (b)**

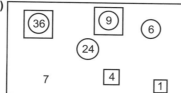

(c) 9 and 36

N54 **(a)** 9 **(b)** 15

(c) 8.2 **(d)** 12.3

N55

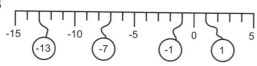

N56 **(a)** -8 > -9 **(b)** -2 < -1

(c) -30 < -20 **(d)** -6 > -15

N57 **(a)** -5 **(b)** -3 **(c)** -10

(d) 14 **(e)** 11 **(f)** -20

N58 **(a) & (c)** **(b)** 12°C

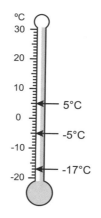

N59 **(a)** 3:9, 5:15, 2:6, 12:36

(b) 6:10, 12:20 **(c)** 14:28 = 1:2

N60 2:3:6 is the same as 4:6:12
1:4:7 is the same as 3:12:21
2:3:5:11 is the same as 6:9:15:33

N61 **(a)** 100 bags **(b)** 250 bags

N62 **(a)** 30 minutes **(b)** 24 minutes

N63

Number of pies	Number of pies to the nearest 10
37	40
13	10
66	70
42	40
144	140
75	80

N64 **(a)** 100 **(b)** 300 **(c)** 400

(d) 600 **(e)** 2400 **(f)** 600

N65 **(a)**

Number of visitors	Number of visitors to the nearest 1000
9392	9000
7828	8000
5539	6000
3998	4000
7299	7000
11 290	11 000
14 599	15 000

(b) 11 000

N66 **(a)** 3 **(b)** 5 **(c)** 28

(d) 3 **(e)** 23 **(f)** 56

Answers

NUMBER

N67 **(a)** Hammer = £6, Saw = £15
Screwdriver = £2, Pliers = £4

(b) Hammer = £6.30, Saw = £14.50
Screwdriver = £2.00, Pliers = £3.60

N68 **(a)** 1.4 **(b)** 0.4 **(c)** 0.8

(d) 14.7 **(e)** 1.8 **(f)** 94.0

N69 **(a)** 1.4 **(b)** 9.9 **(c)** 4.9 **(d)** 7.7

N70 **(a)** 10 **(b)** 10

N71 **(a)** 12 **(b)** 6

ALGEBRA

A1 **(a)** £110 **(b)** £115 **(c)** £180

A2 **(a)** 1 **(b)** 21 **(c)** 28

A3 **(a)** 15 **(b)** 16 **(c)** 4

A4 **(a)** 5 **(b)** 20 **(c)** $\frac{n}{5} + 3$

A5 **(a)** 8 **(b)** 11

A6 **(a)** $5a$ **(b)** $2b$ **(c)** $7c + 2$ **(d)** $5d + 1$

A7 **(a)** $11x + 2y$ **(b)** $10x + 3y$

(c) $x + 5y + 10$ **(d)** $x + 2y + 3$

A8

Person	Number of Books
John	N
Don	$N + 4$
Fern	$N - 2$
Total	$3N + 2$

A9

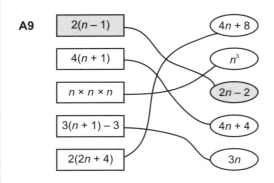

A10 **(a)** 10 **(b)** 4 **(c)** 8

A11 6 kg

A12 **(a)** $x = 3$ **(b)** $x = 2$ **(c)** $x = 2$

A13 **(a)** $y = 10$ **(b)** $y = 4$

A14 **(a)** $2 \times n + 5 = 17$ **(b)** $n = 6$

A15 **(a)** Add 2 to the previous term.

(b) Double the previous term.

(c) The difference is increasing by one each
time, so add 5 to 15 to get the next term.

A16 **(a)** 7, 9 **(b)** 10, 15 **(c)** 27, 81

A17 36, 49, 64

A18 **(a)** **(c)**

(b)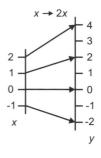

A19 **(a)** n **(b)** $3n$

(c) $3n - 1$ **(d)** $5n - 1$

A20 A (6,1) B (-6,0)

C (-5,-7) D(-4,5)

E (0,-6) F (8, -2)

A21 **(a)**

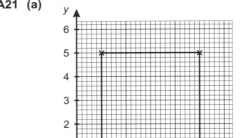

(b) Square

A22 **(a)**

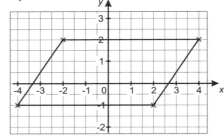

(b) Parallelogram

A23

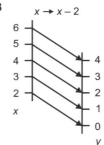

A24 **(a)**

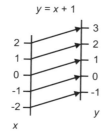

$y = x + 1$

(b) (2,3), (1,2), (0,1), (-1,0), (-2,-1)

(c)

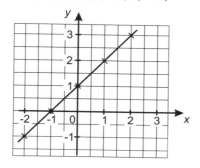

A25 1, -1, 0.5

A26

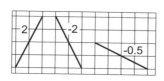

A27 **(a)**

x	0	1	2	3
$y = 2x$	0	2	4	6

(b)

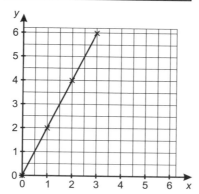

A28

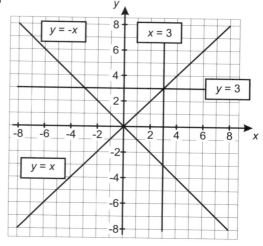

A29 **(a)** IRu200 **(b)** £3.50

A30 **(a)** 2.5 km **(b)** 10 minutes **(c)** B to P

A31 $x = 2.5$

S1 **(a)** **(i)** 4.5 cm

(ii)

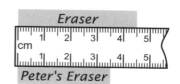

(b) 4 cm

S2 **(a)** 1.7 kg **(b)**

S3 **(a)** 18:30

(b)

S4 **(a)** 11:02

(b) 3 hours 15 minutes

S5 **(a)** Sign 1 has 2 lines of symmetry.
Sign 2 has 3 lines of symmetry.
Sign 3 has 4 lines of symmetry.
Sign 4 has no lines of symmetry.

(b) 2, 3, 4, 1

Answers

S6 **(a)**

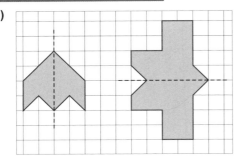

(b)

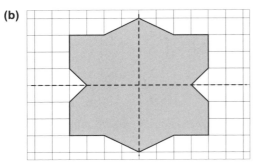

S7

Name	Sketch	Number of lines of symmetry	Order of rotational symmetry
equilateral triangle		3	3
rectangle		2	2
square		4	4
regular hexagon		6	6
regular pentagon		5	5

S8 B

S9 Tetrahedron, cube

S11 **(a)** Gym **(b)** East **(c)** North-west

S12 **(a)**

| Rectangle | Square |

Parallelogram Trapezium

Kite Rhombus

(b) Kite

S13 **(a)** 180° **(b)** 31°

S14 **(a)** 360° **(b)** 99°

S15 **(a)** 14 cm **(b)** 20 cm

     (c) 18 cm **(d)** 30 cm

S16 **(a)** 16 cm **(b)** 24 cm **(c)** 28 cm

S17 **(a)** 18.8 cm (1 dp) **(b)** 31.4 cm (1 dp)

S18 **(a)** 12 cm^2 **(b)** 18 cm^2

     (c) 16 cm^2 **(d)** 10 cm^2

S19 **(a)** 24 cm^2 **(b)** 24 cm^2

S20 **(a)** 14 cm^2 **(b)** 22 cm^2

S21 **(a)** 38 cm^2 **(b)** 60 cm^2

S22 **(a)** 78.5 cm^2 (1 dp) **(b)** 63.6 cm^2 (1 dp)

S23 **(a)** 16 cm^3 **(b)** 18 cm^3

S24 **(a)** height × width × length

     (b) 42 cm^3

S25 255 cm^3

S26 **(a)** 37° **(b)** 145°

     (c) Acute **(d)** Obtuse

S27 **(a)** 90° **(b)** 180° **(c)** 360°

S28 **(a)** 60° **(b)** 15° **(c)** 125°

     (d) 48° **(e)** 50° **(f)** 130°

S30 **(a)** 520 cm **(b)** 230 mm **(c)** 3.2 m

S31 **(a)** 800 g **(b)** 2.4 kg

S32 **(a)** 1200 ml **(b)** 3 litres

S33 **(a)** 120 g **(b)** 1.5 pints

S34 **(a)** 6.25 miles **(b)** 1.8 m

S35 **(a)** 3 m (about twice her height)

     (b) 4.5 m (about three times her height)

S36 **(a)** 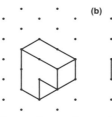 **(b)**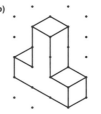

     (c)

 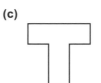

front elevation   side elevation   top elevation

Answers

S37 **(a)**

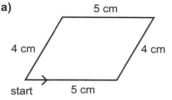

(b) Parallelogram

(c) REPEAT 2 [FORWARD 5, LEFT TURN 60, FORWARD 4, LEFT TURN 120]

S38

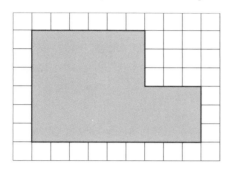

S39

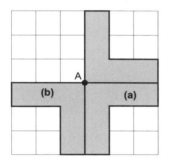

S40

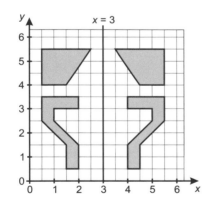

S41 **(a)** G   **(b)** E

     (c) B and F   **(d)** 180°

S42 **(a)** Parallelogram

S43

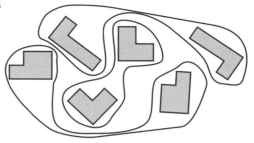

H1 **(a)**

III	IIII II	IIII	III	I
3	7	4	3	1

(b) 18

(c) 5 portions a day makes 35 portions a week, so none of the people surveyed ate enough fruit or vegetables.

H2 **(a)** 0

(b) No, it looks like she never scores any goals.

H3 **(a)** 88 kg   **(b)** 84 kg

(c) The mode, it's the lowest weight.

H4 4

H5 **(a)** 14 mm   **(b)** 87 mm

H6 **(a)** 2   **(b)** 17

H7 **(a)**

IIII I	IIII II	IIII I	III
6	7	6	3

(b)

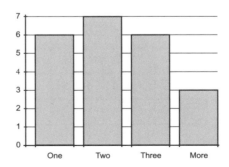

H8 **(a)** 12°C   **(b)** Wednesday

(c) Monday & Friday   **(d)** Saturday

Answers

H9

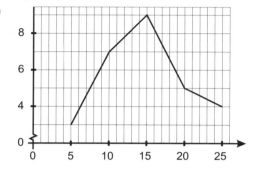

H10 (a) $\frac{1}{8}$ (b) 100   (c) 300

H11

88	22	18	52	**180**
176	44	36	104	**360°**

(a)   (b) $\frac{1}{10}$

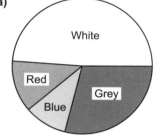

H12 5 cm

H13 (a) Trainees that are good at typing are also good at shorthand (positive correlation).

(b) 35%

H14 (a) Very unlikely   (b) Certain

(c) Evens

H15 (a) (i) White   (ii) More white than grey

(b)

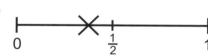

H16 (a) $\frac{7}{15}$ (b) $\frac{8}{15}$

H17 (a)

+	1	2	3	4	5	6
2	3	4	5	6	7	8
3	4	5	6	7	8	9

(b) (i) $\frac{1}{6}$ (ii) $\frac{5}{12}$ (iii) 0

Mental Arithmetic

M1	8	**M2**	3206	**M3**	200 cm
M4	14	**M5**	90 degrees	**M6**	5270
M7	14	**M8**	£6.60	**M9**	21 cm
M10	240 mins	**M11**	Green	**M12**	$\frac{1}{4}$
M13	77%	**M14**	£44	**M15**	$5x$
M16	6	**M17**	13	**M18**	40 mins
M19	55 degrees	**M20**	-10°C	**M21**	18
M22	0.31	**M23**	2	**M24**	C
M25	28	**M26**	£2.03	**M27**	$\frac{1}{4}$
M28	17	**M29**	Rectangle	**M30**	25

Formulae Sheet

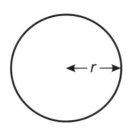

Circle: πr^2

(use $\pi = 3.14$ or your calculator button)

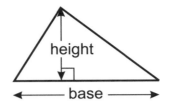

Triangle: $\dfrac{\text{base} \times \text{height}}{2}$

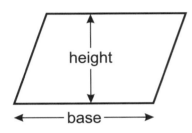

Parallelogram: base × height

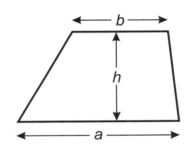

Trapezium: $\dfrac{(a+b)}{2} \times h$

Length Formulae

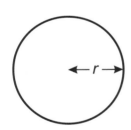

Circle: circumference = $2\pi r$

Volume Formulae

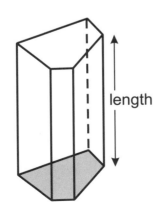

Prism: area of cross-section × length

Mental Mathematics Answer Sheet

M1 ....

M2 ....

M3 .... cm

M4 ....

M5 .... degrees

M6 ....

M7 ....

52.7

$p + 31 = 45$

M8 £ ....

M9 .... cm

M10 .... mins

M11 ....

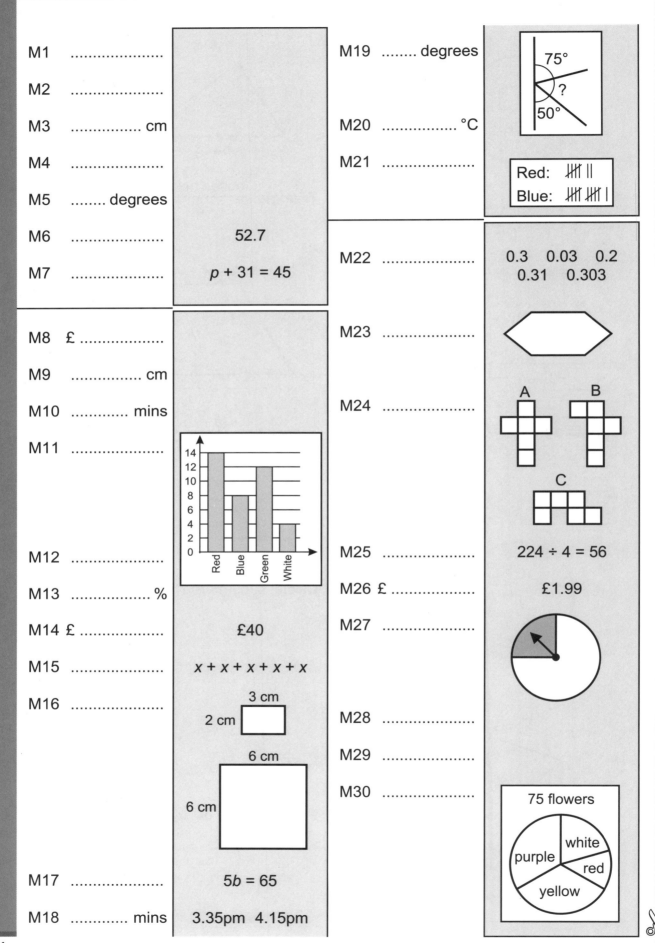

M12 ....

M13 .... %

M14 £ ....

£40

$x + x + x + x + x$

M15 ....

M16 ....

3 cm

2 cm

6 cm

6 cm

M17 ....

$5b = 65$

M18 .... mins   3.35pm 4.15pm

M19 .... degrees

75°

?

50°

Red: |||| ||

Blue: |||| |||| |

M20 .... °C

M21 ....

M22 ....

0.3   0.03   0.2
0.31   0.303

M23 ....

M24 ....

A   B

C

224 ÷ 4 = 56

M25 ....

M26 £ ....

£1.99

M27 ....

M28 ....

M29 ....

M30 ....

75 flowers

white
purple
red
yellow